MW00630222

30 years

——————| *of cartooning* |——————

by David Fitzsimmons

Published by the Arizona Daily Star,
A Lee Enterprises Newspaper,
Tucson, Arizona 2018

ISBN: 978-1-7320616-0-6

© 2018 Arizona Daily Star
tucson.com

All rights reserved.

No part of this book may be reprinted or reproduced in any form, including electronic form,
without the permission of the Arizona Daily Star.

Book design by Maria Camou de Toledo, Arizona Daily Star
Edited by Sarah Garrecht Gassen, Arizona Daily Star

Dedication

"This book is dedicated first, to my 7th grade history teacher, Mrs. Terry Bagwell, and every educator who works tirelessly to shape all of the misbehaving doodlers in the back of the classroom into pretty good citizens. And second, to Steve Auslander, who took a chance, hired me, and gave me a dream job."

Preface

Fitz has a great job.

He is paid to wield a big brush dripping with ink. A few doodle marks here and there and, voila, he has us chuckling about a politician's big ears or wild hair. And paragraphs — those are for authors who fret over the fine points of criticism. Fitz needs just a few words to incite or delight us. What a gig!

Except for the reading, looking and listening part of the job. David's mind is in the "on" position way beyond an eight-hour workday. He reads everything from the news to novels and graffiti. He attends hundreds — yes, hundreds — of events each year to talk to readers and sources. He spars with people on Facebook and on the phone.

David sorts through that cacophony to condense his analysis into a point we "get" at once. Nearly 40 years after we first met as University of Arizona students, I still do not understand how he is able to do it — or how he has the energy. What I have learned is that it takes a smart journalist to create a cartoon five times a week.

— Bobbie Jo Buel, former editor of the Arizona Daily Star

When people find out I work with Fitz, they usually ask a variation of the same question: "Is he always like that? You know, on?"

The answer is no, he's not always "on." He's not a human hybrid of MAD Magazine and Guy Smiley — at least not all the time.

David is a smart, wry and caring guy with a giant heart and an absurdity detector that runs on overdrive 24/7.

And he works from home.

Love him or loathe him, it's nigh impossible to not have an opinion about David Fitzsimmons and his cartoons.

Readers who contact the Star typically want Fitz fired yesterday or declared a national treasure.

In fact, I was just interrupted by a phone call from an irate man who declared, in increasing decibels and increasingly colorful language, that David Fitzsimmons is an abomination and a disgrace and an embarrassment, and a ... well, you get the drift. It comes with the territory. The Star also publishes conservative syndicated cartoonists, but those don't garner the same intensity of response as Fitz's homegrown arrow-slinging.

But some of Fitz's best work has nothing to do with politics, and you'll find many reader favorites in this book. The "Code of the Saguaro" captures our desert home, and the world from a quail's point of view makes me laugh every time. I hope they make you chuckle, too.

— Sarah Garrecht Gassen, Editorial Page editor of the Arizona Daily Star

David Fitzsimmons, The Arizona Daily Star

First cartoon to appear in the Star after Fitz was hired as the Star's full-time cartoonist.

"WE GOT US A LIVE CARTOONIST"

So read the proud headline on the Arizona Daily Star opinion page Jan. 5, 1986. Above the column introducing me to the readers like a prized marlin was my first cartoon, predicting that this new phenomena — global terrorism — would dominate the news.

Thirty-plus years, 47 paper cuts and 9,000 cartoons later, I am the luckiest "live cartoonist" I know, syndicated globally, and still afflicting the comfortable and comforting the afflicted in a field vanishing faster than a popsicle on a Tucson sidewalk in June.

There were more than 200 political cartoonists in the country back when I was drawing Ike on my nursery wall with a crayon. Today, the 40 of us could hold our annual convention in a Teardrop camper. Make that 39. Oops. 38.

As long as I can remember, I've wanted to be a political cartoonist. Or a desert garden landscaper. Or a preacher. Or an obstetrician, according to an essay I wrote when I was at Myers Elementary School, a fine public school where my delightful fifth-grade teacher, Mr. Archie Burke, taught me how to draw a witty caricature of Lyndon Baines Johnson out of his initials. This feat won the heart of the girl who sat next to me drawing unicorns, flowers and butterflies. I was hooked on drawing presidents. And Boris and Natasha.

My next crush was on Mrs. Terry Bagwell, my seventh-grade history teacher. Catching me sketching when I should have been paying attention — for the millionth time — she asked me if there was something amusing I'd care to share with the rest of the group. I froze, imagining my furious father, the Master Sergeant, at home.

I gulped, panicked, foresaw a life in prison, and desperately tried to hide the evidence.

Confiscating that masterpiece, the loveliest educator in all of Naylor Middle School suggested I might redirect my disruptive knack for cartooning in a more positive direction. "Give the yearbook staff a try. After school. They could use a cartoonist." It was that afternoon, in that place, where I found my kith, my kin and my avocation: nerds and newsrooms.

My first editorial cartoons were published in the Rincon Echo at Rincon High School.

At the same time, my anti-war cartoons were

Fitzsimmons

welcomed in a local underground paper, The Frumious Bandersnatch. The founder, the late Hugh Holub, told me the FBI kept files on us.

As the Sixties were rioting to a close, Mr. Freeman Hover at Rincon taught us, issue after issue, to appreciate why journalism and the truth were so important to the health of our democracy.

I didn't get it then. I get it now.

When I was a freshman at the University of Arizona, drifting between media majors and heading into ROTC, I was surprised to get an unsolicited invitation from the Arizona Daily Wildcat to be their staff cartoonist. My mother — how embarrassing! — had secretly submitted a portfolio of my work.

Thanks, Mom.

The idea carnival comes to town

I wake up every day to NPR. I get up, brush my teeth and channel surf MSNBC, FOX and CNN until my fake sausage is microwaved. I join my wife at the table so I can steal sips from her coffee and study the Arizona Daily Star like a Talmudic scholar.

A brisk walk around my neighborhood — my answer to the daily commute ritual — stirs the blood and the cauldron twixt my ears that's bubbling with cartoon ideas.

By the time I'm back, everyone's off to school or work.

I head down the hall to my silent studio, where I binge on internet news, the latest tweets and Facebook postings.

And then I stare at the blank paper on my drawing board.

On most days, cartoon ideas roll out of my head like chocolates on a conveyor belt in a Lucille Ball comedy sketch. Sometimes riding my bike or driving my car invites the cartoon idea carnival to town.

I like to begin with at least five or six good concepts percolating, which I can take to the drawing board, doodle into cartoon life, refine or reject. I've never missed a deadline. For every cartoon that makes it to print, there are reams of duds in the recycling basket.

By mid-morning I will have found an idea I want to draw. I've decided on the characters, the plot, the dialogue and the setting. I like to start with the eyes because I can reveal so much with the eyes.

I use Eberhart-Faber flexible nib pens, a responsive pen that allows me to draw with flourish, creating the illusion the drawing was inked into existence in seconds by an old Warner Brothers pro.

When I first started drawing, I drew in a tedious photorealistic style that relied on pointillist dots and took hours. Today I love drawing in a graphic and bold Hanna-Barbera retro style. It's fun to cloak unpalatable sedition in sugary sweet modernist imagery right out of the all-American Jetsons and Flintstones visual vocabulary.

On a good day, I'm the fastest draw west of the San Pedro. On other days, I'm slower than a desert tortoise, taking six to eight hours to produce a drawing that has just the right color, punch, composition and appearance of spontaneity.

Without such correspondence a cartoonist may suffer despondence

At my first cartoonists conference, I whined to the old cartoonist at the bar about getting hate mail. "Some readers actually hate my cartoons," I said.

The old, grizzled ink slingers looked at me like I was a complete failure. One of the older ink-stained doodlers muttered, "That's your job. To provoke a reaction."

So, yes, I get hate mail. And, yes, I love it.

The question I am asked most often is "Why can't you be fair?" which roughly translates into "Why can't you stop picking on my political heroes for once and instead attack your own!" Good luck with that idea. Send the same pleas to Rush Limbaugh or Jon Stewart and imagine their response.

When I got my first of many hand-scrawled death threats, I was astonished that mere lines on paper could provoke violent reactions.

I've never regretted a cartoon and will never defend or explain one. If a cartoon does not speak for itself, it is a failed cartoon.

It's true, keen observer. I am unfair. I will not argue points of view with which I disagree. I draw only what I believe. I feel no need to be charitable toward opinions and actions I find repugnant.

I shall be a progressive voice harping on reforming immigration, lifting up public education and spotlighting social injustice until they pry my pen from my dead, cold, ink-stained fingers.

Holy jalapeños

You can see my personality in my Arroyo Cafe characters, and in my desert rats, the nerdy quail and the goofy javelina. To varying degrees, they are all self-portraits. What we all share is a deep love for the Old Pueblo and this extraordinary desert.

When I graduated from the University of Arizona in 1977, Steve Auslander, then the Editorial Page editor of the Arizona Daily Star, told me there was no budget for a cartoonist.

I would be in exile for a decade, sending my political cartoons and letters of inquiry off to oblivion by night, and, by day, working at newspapers as a mapmaker, then a photo re-toucher, then an illustrator, typographer and graphic designer.

After bouncing around the country, the Arizona Daily Star caved to my relentless campaign, which had been propelled by unmitigated homesickness.

I finally returned to the place I love.

Tucson is salsa. The rest of the world is mayonnaise.

— David Fitzsimmons, 2018

Arizona

Fitz feasts on the mystery that is the Arizona Legislature and state government — specifically its Republican majority.

Fitz nails tough issues that range from Arizona Senate Bill 1070 (aka the "show me your papers" bill) to perpetually inadequate public school funding to President Obama tapping Democratic Gov. Janet Napolitano to serve in his cabinet, which left Arizona Secretary of State Jan Brewer, a Republican, as governor. He weighs in on the Legislature's overreach into local school district matters, such as with his cartoon noting the court decision that the "ethnic studies law" aimed at the Tucson Unified School District's Mexican American Studies program was created with racist intent. Fitz nailed it all with his ability to say in an image what it takes us mere mortals too many words to explain.

Bees of ARIZona

NORMAL Bee   KILLER Bee   BisBee

Fitzsimmons

Fitzsimmons

~ARPAIO PAPER DOLL~

LEGAL DEFENSE BALONEY SANDWICH

NEW OFFICIAL UNIFORM

"HUSKY BOY" PINK UNDERWEAR

BALL AND CHAIN

DISGRACE TO LAW ENFORCEMENT

FITZSIMMONS @THE ARIZONA DAILY STAR 2017 CAGLECARTOONS.com

Fitzsimmons

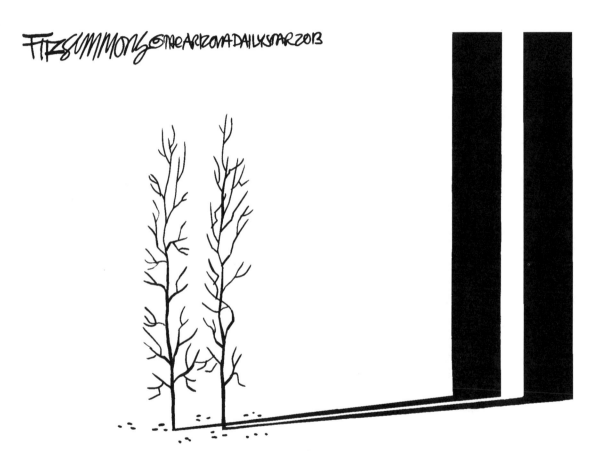

THE COURAGE OF THE YARNELL FIREFIGHTERS

OUR LEGISLATOR'S SOLEMN VOW

I PLEDGE ALLEGIANCE TO	and THAT FOR WHICH IT STANDS	WITH	FOR
☐ MY WINGNUT CONSTITUENTS	☐ DISASTER	☐ JUSTICE AND LIBERTY AND TAX BREAKS	☐ MY CORPORATE DONORS
☐ GROVER NORQUIST AND HIS ANTI-TAX CABAL	☐ ONE NATION UNDER FOX	☐ GUNS	☐ ALL
☐ RUSH	☐ ONE STATE UNDER A SUICIDE WATCH	☐ A KICK IN THE SHORTS	☐ WHAT'S LEFT OF PUBLIC EDUCATION
		☐ DISDAIN	

FITZSIMMONS © THE ARIZONA DAILY STAR 2009

General

Fitz's world view comes through loud and clear in his cartoons. He's always been an advocate for public education, kids, immigrants, families struggling to get by and people targeted for being who they are. He speaks the truth, as he sees it, in plain visual language, holding those in power accountable. Whether it's pointing out the failures of our public institutions by skewering the Tucson Unified School District's leadership or weighing in on the consequences of the 9/11 attacks, Fitz doesn't pull his punches.

Fitzsimmons

OUT OF THE RUINS

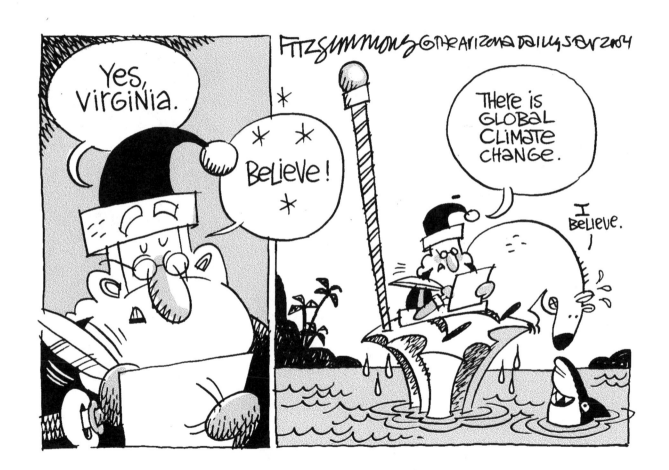

HOW ABOUT A LITTLE SOMETHING TO HELP OUR SAD FRIEND HOLD HIMSELF TOGETHER IN THESE DIFFICULT TIMES. A FEW BILLION? A TRILLION? WHATEVER YOU CAN SPARE.

ON MEMORIAL DAY WE REMEMBER

WHEN WILL IT EVER END?

WHAT DID YOU DO IN SCHOOL TODAY?

in Biology we studied tourniquets and blood flow.

in Government we memorized the 2nd Amendment.

in MATH we studied bullet velocity.

in P.E. we practiced running in our kevlar vests.

in DRAMA we rehearsed "Annie get your gun."

in English we wrote a persuasive ESSAY pleading with a shooter to spare our lives.

in Health class we had a quiz on mass shooting statistics.

I did my homework. can I go play "urban warzone" on my computer?

Fitzsimmons ©THE ARIZONA DAILY STAR 2015 CAGLECARTOONS.com

BILL COSBY'S GREATEST HITS
ALL IN THIS ONE AMAZING ALBUM SET TO BE RELEASED ANY DAY NOW!

BILLCOSBY
IS A VERY CREEPY FELLOW
RIGHT !

Produced by BILL COSBY

Side one

New Girlfriend - 0:51
Ludes - 2:31
Wrestling - 1:31
Nap Time - 4:21
The Devil Made Him Do It - 0:58
The Lone Ranger - 3:07
Prescription Refill - 1:53

Side two

Frizzle Frazzle Gossip - 3:45
Girls and Wonderfulness - 0:59
Out to Get Me - 5:45
An Innocent Man - 0:45
The Neanderthal - 6:44
Zippity Lippity - 4:45
Prison Pudding- 3:48

FITZSIMMONS©THEARIZDAILYSTAR2015

Fitzsimmons

IN RESPONSE TO THE HORRIFIC GUN CARNAGE A **MOMENT** OF SILENCE WILL BE OBSERVED.

NRA

A MOMENT THAT WILL LAST AS LONG AS THE CHECKS KEEP COMING.

FITZSIMMONS © THE ARIZONA DAILY STAR 2016 caglecartoons.com

Fitzsimmons

More people have been Slaughtered in the name of religion than for any other single reason. That, my friends, is true perversion.

—Harvey Milk

ORLANDO

Fitzsimmons

Fitzsimmons

Immigration

L ooking through Fitz's 30 years of work at the Arizona Daily Star, a couple of things become clear: Arizona has always struggled with public education funding and immigration has always been a hot topic, nationally and at home. Fitz has aimed his pen at the undercurrent of racism and anti-Latino sentiment he sees as the root of the Arizona Legislature's attempts to usurp federal immigration laws, such as Senate Bill 1070. And he reminds us that the highest cost of Congress failing to create a common sense and workable immigration system is paid by the thousands of migrants who've died in the Sonoran Desert in Southern Arizona as they sought work or were fleeing violence at home.

ANOTHER CROSSER DIES IN A DESERT

CROSSING THROUGH ARIZONA

Fitzsimmons

January 8, 2011

W hen a young man with severe, and untreated, mental illness walked up to a crowd gathered to speak with U.S. Rep. Gabrielle Giffords at a Congress on Your Corner event and started shooting, Tucson was stunned — and we came together.

The assassin shot and killed six Tucsonans: Christina-Taylor Green, 9; Dorothy Morris, 76; U.S. District Judge John M. Roll, 63; Phyllis Schneck, 79; Dorwan Stoddard, 76; and Gabe Zimmerman, 30. He shot Giffords in the head and 12 more Tucsonans also were wounded.

Fitz reflected on the tragedy with sorrow, for the lives shattered and stolen, and with outrage aimed at politicians and the gun lobby who have fought against any changes in gun laws. These gun-related cartoons are a lightning rod, one that Fitz never shies away from.

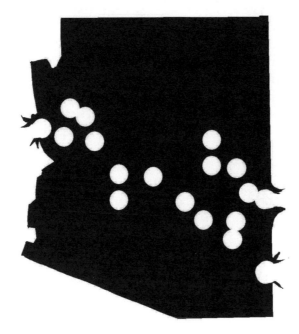

WOUNDED

CLIP and SAVE and PIN TO EVERY POLITICIAN'S FOREHEAD IN AMERICA

FITZSIMMONS © THE ARIZONA DAILY STAR 2012 CAGLECARTOONS.COM.

CHRISTINA-TAYLOR GREEN

THAT'S WHAT I BELIEVE.. BECAUSE THAT'S WHAT CHRISTINA-TAYLOR GREEN BELIEVED. I WANT OUR DEMOCRACY TO BE AS GOOD AS SHE IMAGINED IT.

ALL OF US SHOULD DO EVERYTHING WE CAN TO MAKE SURE THIS COUNTRY LIVES UP TO OUR CHILDREN'S EXPECTATIONS.

I WANT AMERICA TO BE AS GOOD AS SHE IMAGINED IT.

-- PRESIDENT OBAMA
TOGETHER WE THRIVE MEMORIAL EVENT 2011

Fitzsimmons

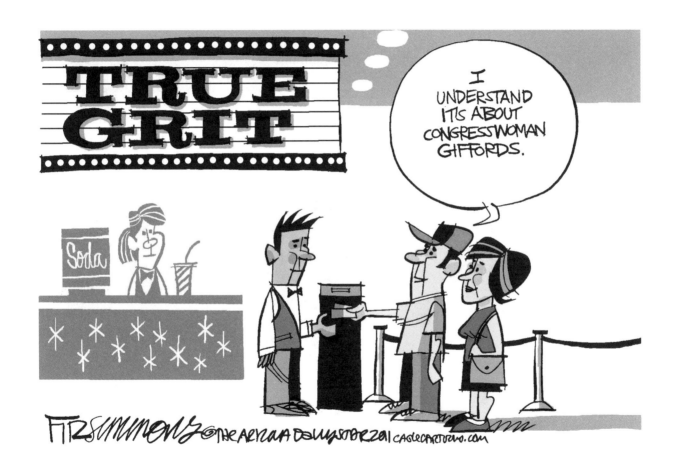

Obituaries

Fitz's gift of cutting to the quick is matched by his summing up of sorrow and an appreciation for a life in a singular image. He gets to the heart of a person, even those he might have vociferously disagreed with in life. For example, his cartoon of Nancy Reagan being reunited with her beloved Ronald salutes their deep love. From crossword-maker Merl Reagle to Fred Rogers putting up stars with his iconic sweater hanging on the moon in the night sky, Fitz gives us a moment to pause and connect.

IT'S THE HAMMER OF JUSTICE IT'S THE BELL OF FREEDOM IT'S THE SONG OF LOVE BETWEEN MY BROTHERS AND MY SISTERS.

PETE SEEGER 1919-2014

ROBIN WILLIAMS, R.I.P.

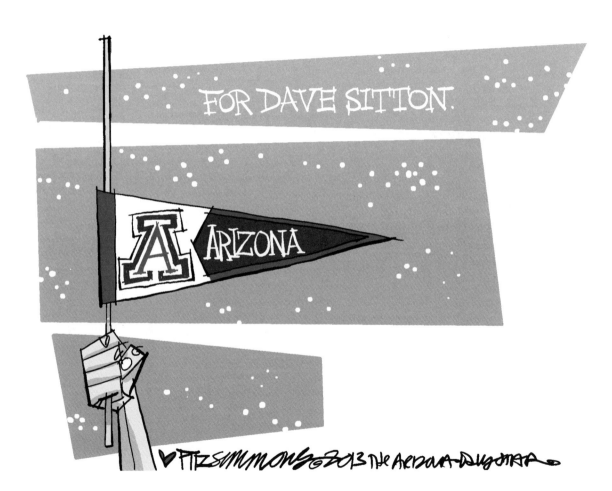

HIGHLIGHTS FROM ANDY ROONEY'S CAREER

WOOLY MAMMOTHS MAKE TERRIBLE PETS.

MOSES. WHAT'S WITH THE PLAGUES?

VIKING HELMETS. WHAT'S WITH THE HORNS?

GARGOYLES ON CATHEDRALS. I LIKE 'EM.

LINCOLN! KEEP THE WHISKERS.

ORVILLE AND WILBUR WRIGHT ARE ON TO SOMETHING.

WHAT EYEBROWS?

THESE BABIES WILL NEVER RETIRE.

FITZSIMMONS © THE ARIZONA DAILY STAR 2011 CAGLECARTOONS.COM

Fitzsimmons

FRED ROGERS
1929-2003

Fitzsimmons
@THE ARIZONA DAILY STAR
2003

Fitzsimmons

Presidents, Parties and Politics

They're Fitz's bread and butter: the often feckless and hypocritical elected officials who dare to preach one thing and do another, those who should represent their constituents but put their own interests first. Some of Fitz's best work comes from his keen sense of justice and his ability to cut through the talking-points blather and to gut sacred cows.

DECISION POINTS

GEORGE W BUSH

THIS VIAL CONTAINS WHAT'S LEFT OF McCAIN'S INTEGRITY, PALIN'S QUALIFICATIONS TO BE PRESIDENT *and* ENOUGH TOXIC CAMPAIGN MUD TO DRIVE ME TO ENDORSE BARACK OBAMA.

THE OLD REPUBLICAN PARTY.

THE NEW REPUBLICAN PARTY.

MIND YOUR OWN BUSINESS

I LIKE IKE

I ♥ BIG BUSINESS

FITZSIMMONS @ THE ARIZONA DAILY STAR 2013 CAGLE CARTOONS.COM

PROPOSED monument

BRONZE

MARBLE

GRANITE

TEFLON

FITZSIMMONS © The Arizona Daily Star 2004

Fitzsimmons

Fitzsimmons

Fitzsimmons

Fitzsimmons

TRUMP

Fitzsimmons

LET ME BE CLEAR. IT'S NOT OVUH UNTIL EVERY SUPERDELEGATE SINGS! OR I SNAP OUT OF MY DELUSIONAL STATE. WHICHEVUH COMES FIRST.

FANFARE FOR THE NEXT TWO YEARS

On Being a Tucsonan

W e live in a weird place. It rains while the sun shines, we can hit 115 degrees in the summer and freeze in the winter. The clouds can sometimes look like enormous mashed potatoes hovering over the mountains. Fitz captures all of this, and more, when he draws about our desert home and its creatures. From the classic "Code of the Saguaro" to "The Brain of a Tucsonan," Fitz homes in on what makes Tucson such a special place to live.

Fitzsimmons

Your Winter Wardrobe Accessories

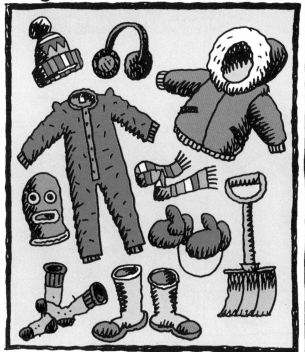

FITZsimmons
@THEARIZONA DAILY STAR

EVERYWHERE ELSE

TUCSON

Tucson's Winter Olympics

Sunglasses Relay | The Lounge | Saltillo Tile Sock Speed Skating

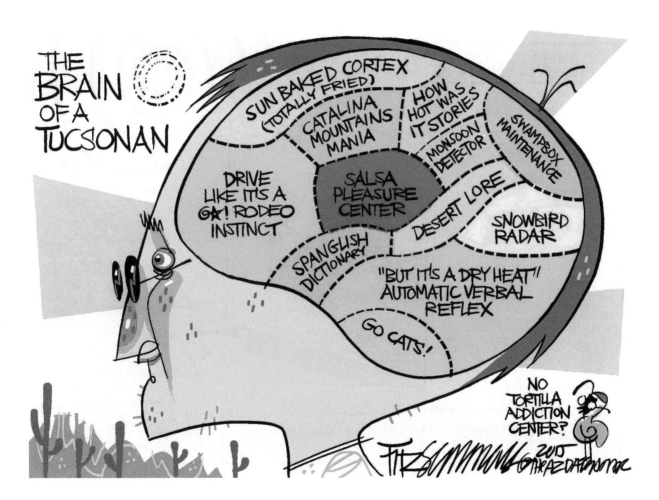

FITZSIMMONS © The Arizona Daily Star 2006

Take Home a ★ FORMER ★ RODEO STAR

Fitzsimmons

SUMMER FASHION IN THE OLD PUEBLO

"CASUAL"   "FORMAL"   "WORK"

ARE YOU PREPARED FOR THE TUCSON FESTIVAL OF BOOKS?

HAT

NPR

SHADES

SUNSCREEN

PARASOL

TFOB APP

WATER

BOOKS TO BE SIGNED BY AUTHORS

STRAND BOOKSTORE

FLARE TO LET FAMILY KNOW YOU'RE STILL ALIVE AND LIVING OFF KETTLE KORN AND BOOKS.

Fitzsimmons

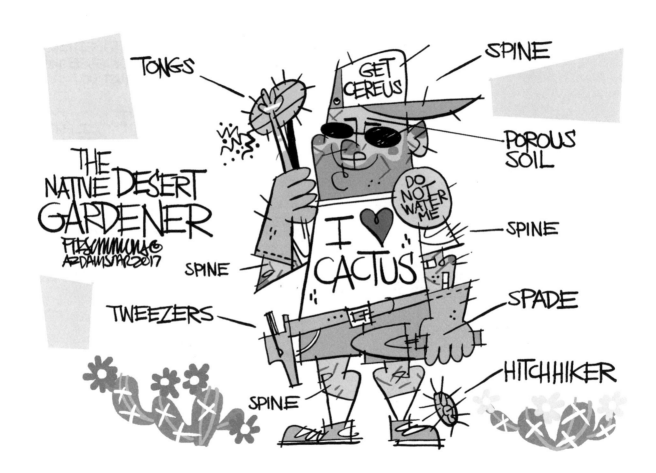

CODE OF THE SAGUARO

BE STRONG.

KEEP A TOUGH EXTERIOR BUT STAY SOFT INSIDE.

ALWAYS KEEP YOUR ARMS OPEN TO THE WORLD.

ALWAYS OFFER SHELTER AND COMFORT TO THE LEAST AMONG US.

BE THRIFTY.

AND MAY YOU ALWAYS STAND TALL IN THE SUNSHINE.

The Arizona Daily Star
tooner@tucson.com

Fitzsimmons

Wildlife & Weather

F itz's quail and javelina are some reader favorites, and with good reason. They're the constants in Fitz's work. As politicians and scandals come and go, our friends the quail and javelina remind us that no matter the news of the day we should look around to see the hope and joy and humor of life.

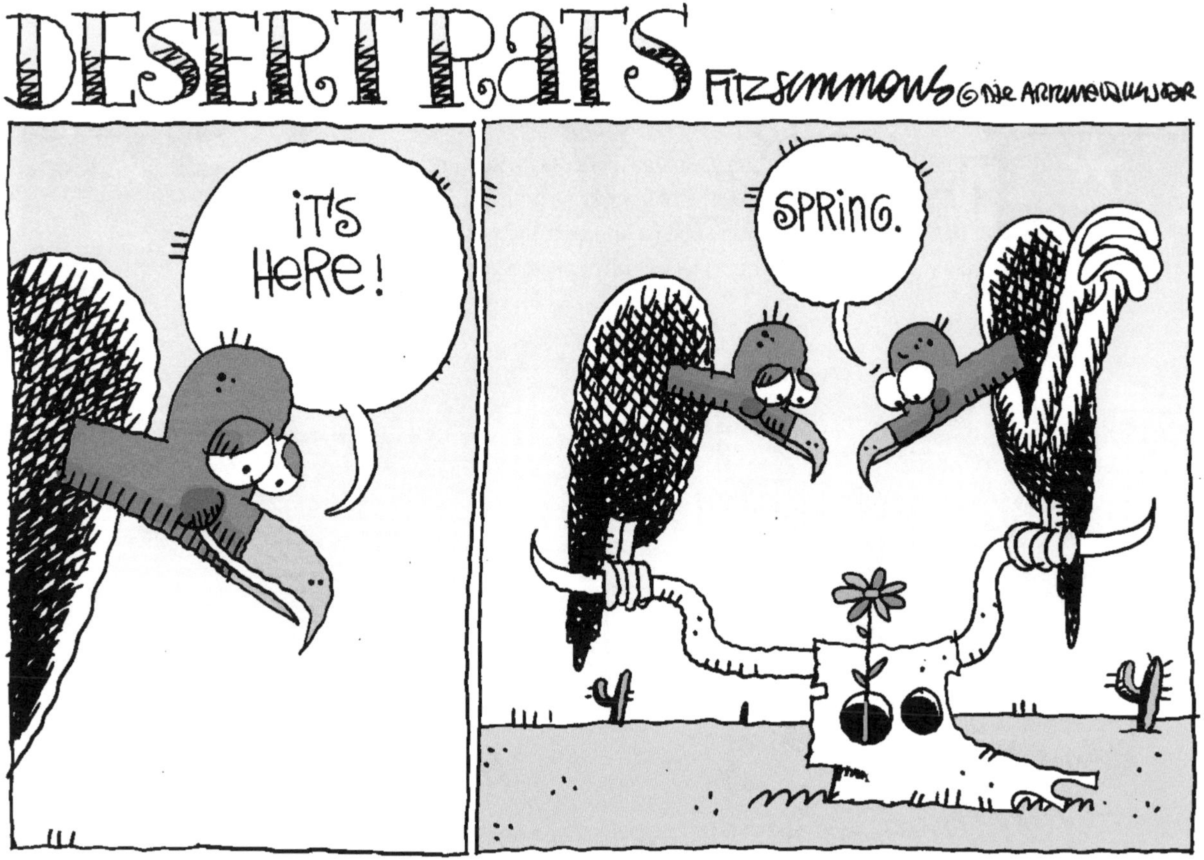
DESERT RATS
FITZSIMMONS
IT'S HERE!
SPRING.

Peccadillo du Peccary

Under The Tusk and Sun

SAGUARO Fruit Wine

@ THE ARIZONA DAILY STAR

FITZSIMMONS

Fitzsimmons

Fitzsimmons

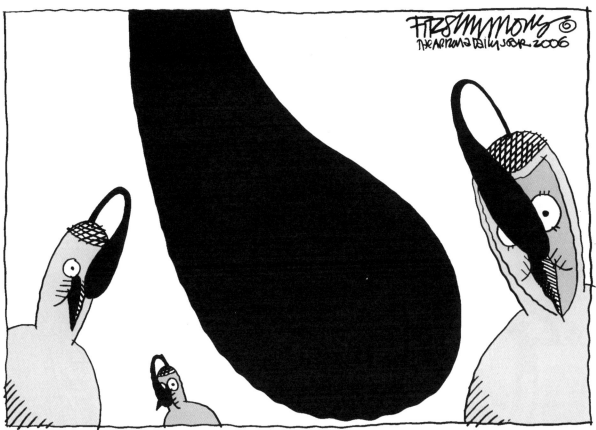

The Quail's eye view

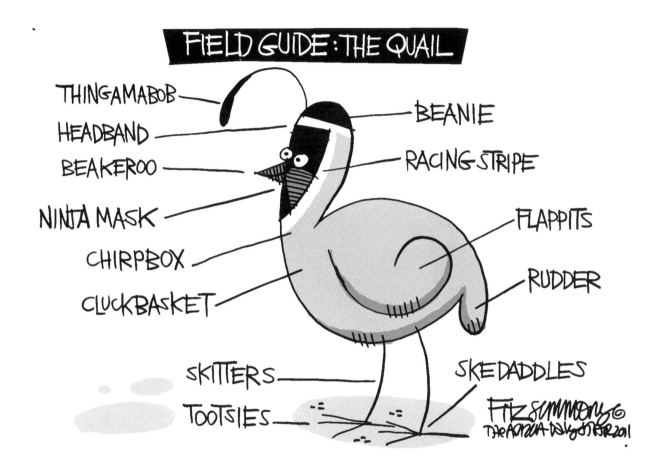

FIELD GUIDE: THE QUAIL

THINGAMABOB

HEADBAND

BEAKEROO

NINJA MASK

CHIRPBOX

CLUCKBASKET

BEANIE

RACING STRIPE

FLAPPITS

RUDDER

SKITTERS

TOOTSIES

SKEDADDLES

A PASSLE OF PECCARY PET PEEVES

1. Nosey quail
2. Herd mentality
3. Vandal-proof Dumpsters
4. Arizona Game and Fish agents
6. Tranquilizer darts
7. "Here, piggy piggy "
8. Expired prickly pear fruit
10. Javelina head trophies
11. Musk cologne for humans
12. Chewy prickly pear